It's Easy To Play James Bond

CW00798135

WISE PUBLICATIONS
part of The Music Sales Group
London / New York / Paris / Sydney / Copenhagen / Berlin / Madrid / Hong Kong / Tokyo

Published by
Wise Publications
14-15 Berners Street, London W1T 3LJ, UK.

Exclusive Distributors:
Music Sales Limited
Distribution Centre, Newmarket Road,
Bury St Edmunds, Suffolk IP33 3YB, UK.
Music Sales Pty Limited
Units 3-4, 17 Willfox Street, Condell Park, NSW 2200, Australia.

Order No. AM1006533
ISBN: 978-1-78305-109-0
This book © Copyright 2013 Wise Publications,
a division of Music Sales Limited.

Compiled and edited by Jenni Norey.
Music arranged by Fiona Bolton.
Music processed by Paul Ewers Music Design.
Cover photographs courtesy of Rex Features.
Printed in the EU.

Your Guarantee of Quality:

As publishers, we strive to produce every book
to the highest commercial standards.

This book has been carefully designed to minimise awkward
page turns and to make playing from it a real pleasure.

Particular care has been given to specifying acid-free, neutral-sized paper made
from pulps which have not been elemental chlorine bleached.
This pulp is from farmed sustainable forests and
was produced with special regard for the environment.

Throughout, the printing and binding have been planned to ensure a sturdy,
attractive publication which should give years of enjoyment.

If your copy fails to meet our high standards,
please inform us and we will gladly replace it.

www.musicsales.com

The James Bond Theme

Music by Monty Norman

swing

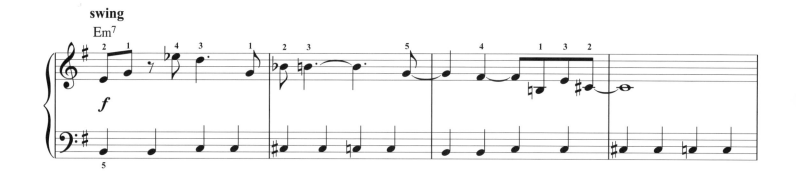

Goldfinger

Words by Leslie Bricusse & Anthony Newley
Music by John Barry

Broadly

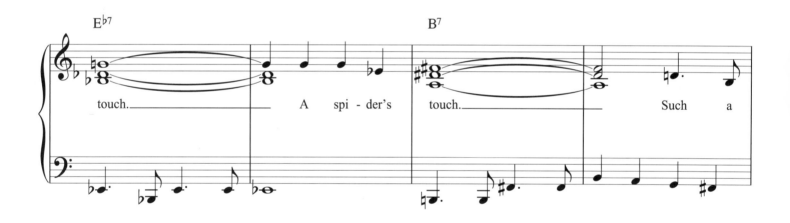

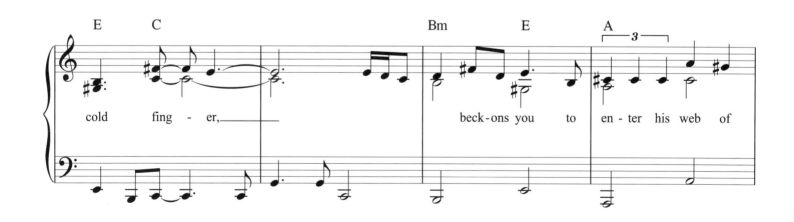

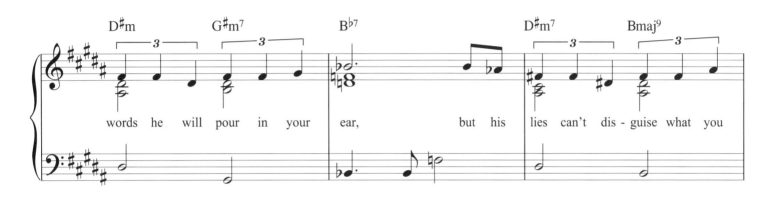

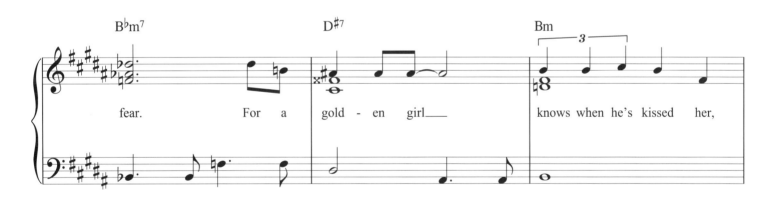

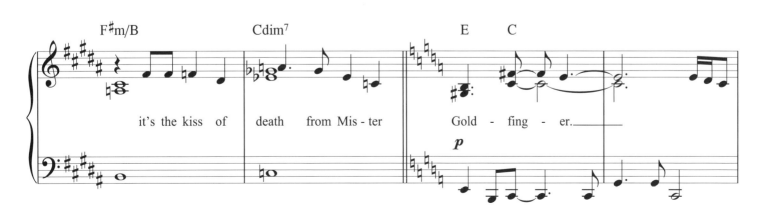

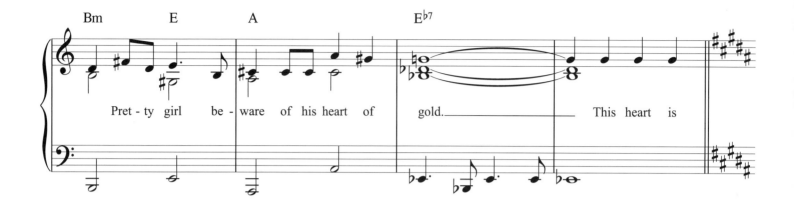

Pret - ty girl be - ware of his heart of gold. This heart is

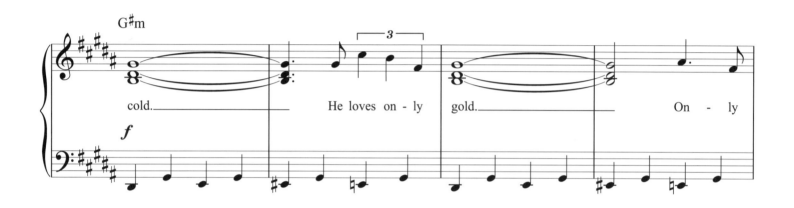

cold. He loves on - ly gold. On - ly

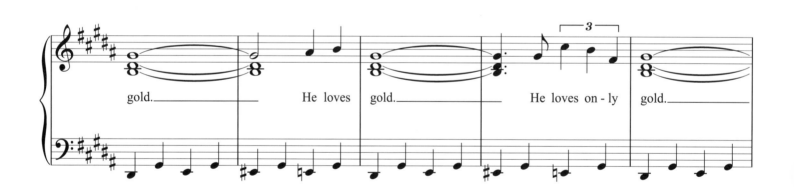

gold. He loves gold. He loves on - ly gold.

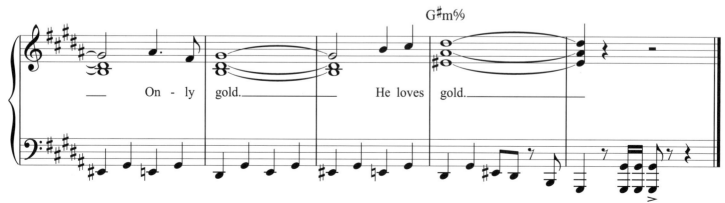

On - ly gold. He loves gold.

You Only Live Twice

Words by Leslie Bricusse
Music by John Barry

One life for your - self and one for your dreams.

You drift through the years and life seems tame

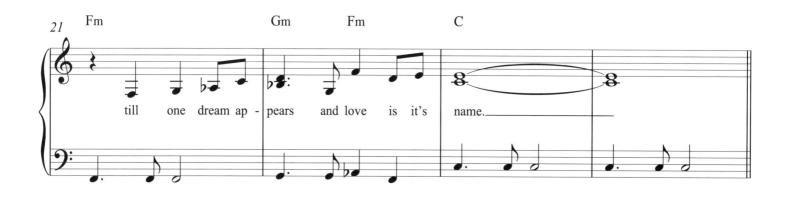

till one dream ap - pears and love is it's name.

And love is a stran - ger who'll beck-on you on.

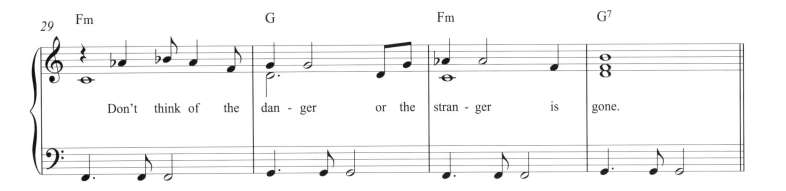

Don't think of the dan - ger or the stran - ger is gone.

This dream is for you so pay the price.

Make one dream come true, you on - ly live twice.___

twice.

We Have All The Time In The World

Words by Hal David
Music by John Barry

14

Diamonds Are Forever

Words by Don Black
Music by John Barry

Live And Let Die

Words & Music by Paul & Linda McCartney

Live and let die,____ live and let

die,____ live and let die.____

ff

To Coda

mf What does it mat - ter to ya,

when you got a job to do____ you got - ta do it well,____ you got - ta

19

give the oth - er fel - low hell!

Nobody Does It Better

Words by Carole Bayer Sager
Music by Marvin Hamlisch

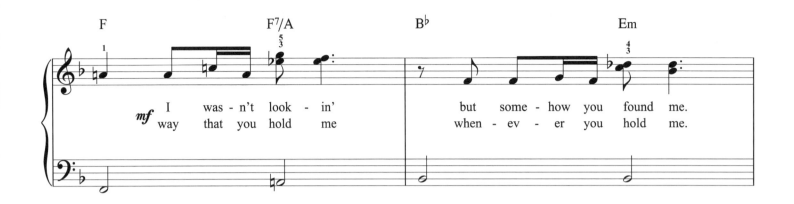

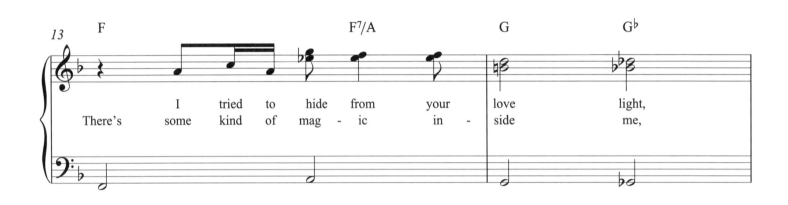

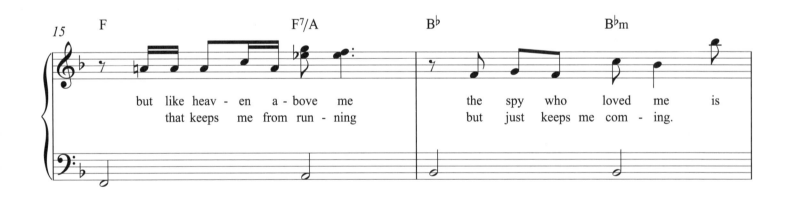

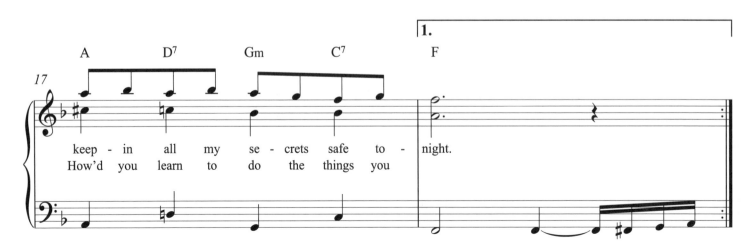

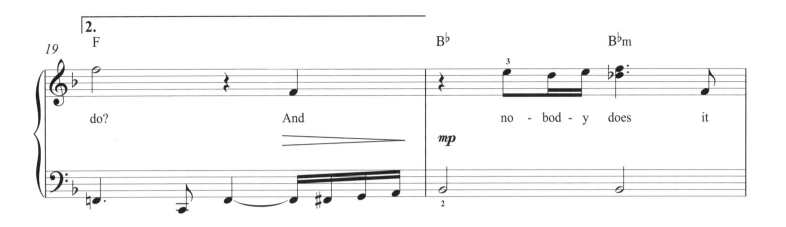

Moonraker

Words by Hal David
Music by John Barry

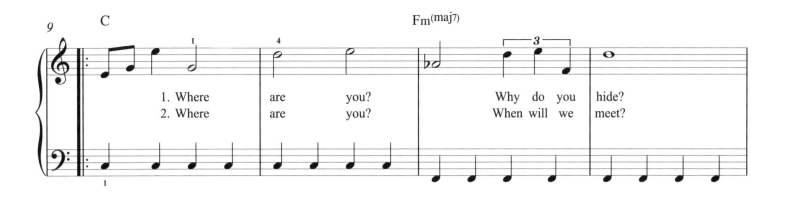

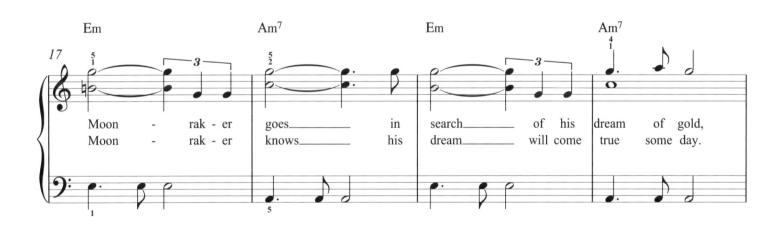

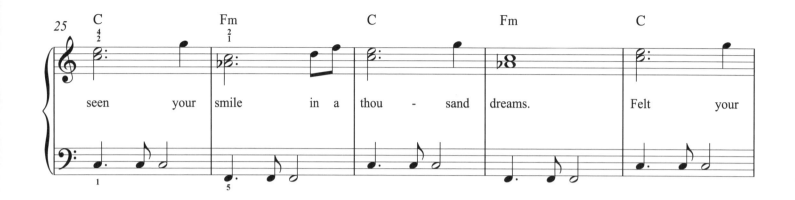

seen your smile in a thou - sand dreams. Felt your

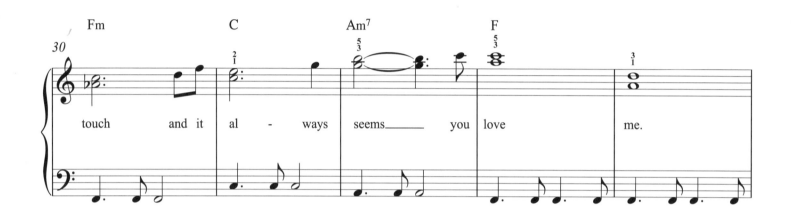

touch and it al - ways seems____ you love me.

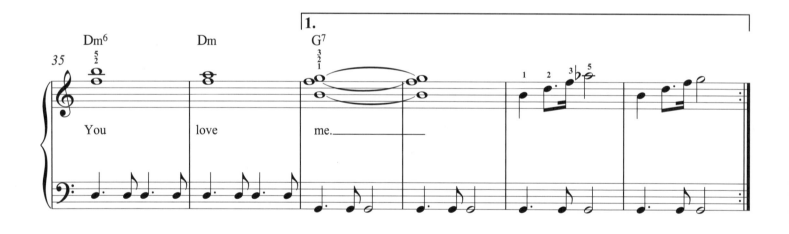

1.

You love me.____

2.

me.____

For Your Eyes Only

Words by Michael Leeson
Music by Bill Conti

love, I know you need - ed me, the fan - ta - sy you freed in me.
pas - sions that col - lide in me, the wild a - ban - doned side of me.

1.

On - ly for you._ On - ly for you. *dim.*

2. For

2.

On - ly for you._ For your eyes on - ly._ *dim.*

p

All Time High

Words by Tim Rice
Music by John Barry

Licence To Kill

Words & Music by John Barry, Leslie Bricusse, Anthony Newley,
Narada Michael Walden, Walter Afanasieff & Jeffrey Cohen

35

Say that some-bod-y tries___ to make a move on you,

in the blink of an eye___ I will be there too.

And they'd bet-ter know why I'm gon-na make 'em pay

till their dy-ing day,___ till their dy-ing day,___

till their dy-ing day.___ Got a

Tomorrow Never Dies

Words & Music by Sheryl Crow & Mitchell Froom

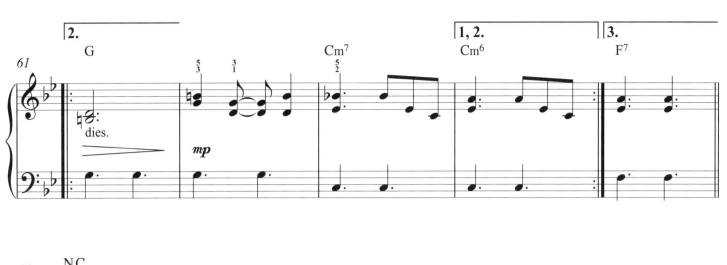

The World Is Not Enough

Words by Don Black
Music by David Arnold

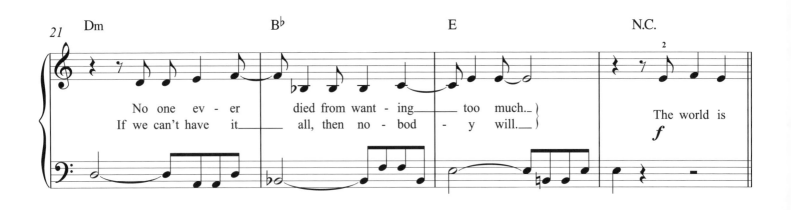

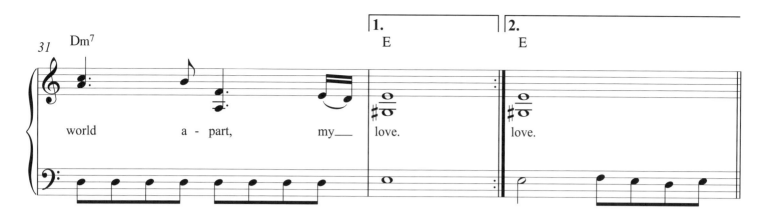

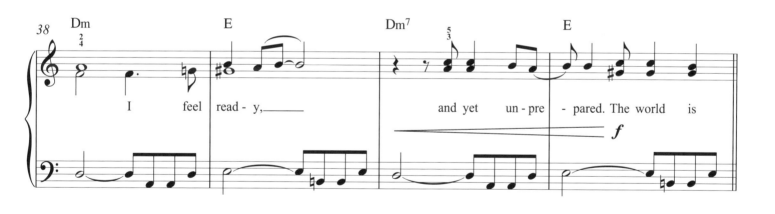

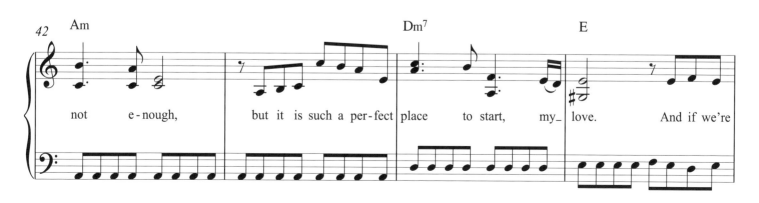

strong e - nough, to - geth - er we can take the world a - part, my___

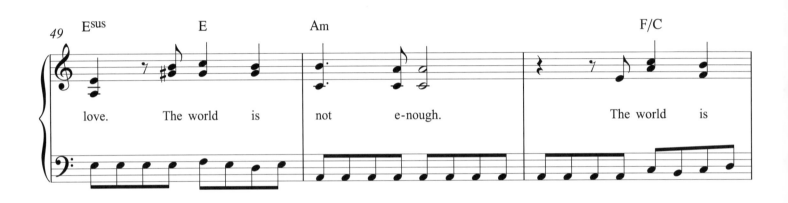

love. The world is not e - nough. The world is

not e - nough. Don't go where he has gone.

The world is not e - nough.

You Know My Name

Words & Music by David Arnold & Chris Cornell

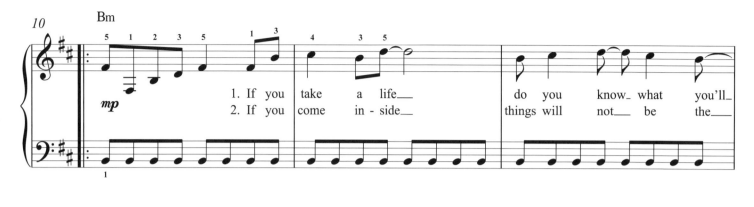

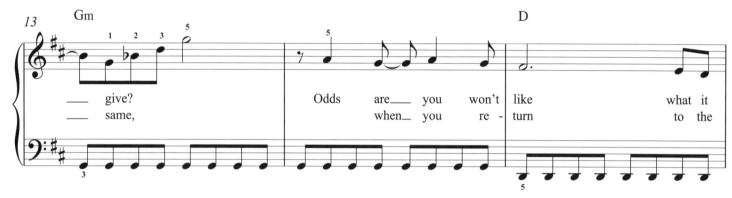

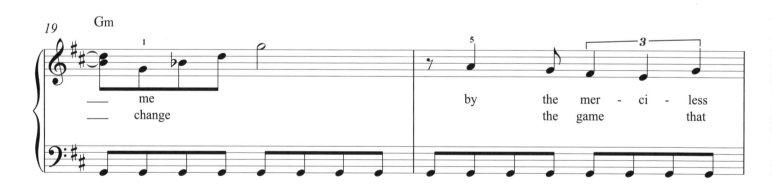

49

Skyfall

Words & Music by Paul Epworth & Adele Adkins

54

(When it crum-bles.)   (We will stand tall.)

Cm(add9)
(Let the sky fall.)   (When it crum-bles.)

Cm   Fm9
(We will stand tall.)   Where you go   I go,   what you see

Abmaj7   Cm/Bb   Cm/B
I see.   I know I'd   nev-er be____ me____ with-out the se-

Cm   Cm/Bb   Abmaj7   Cm/G
-cu - ri - ty____   of your lov-ing arms   keep-ing

23456789